STAR OF WONDER

A Christmas musical for young children

Barry Hart

kevin mayhew

We hope you enjoy *Star of Wonder*. Further copies are available from your local music shop or Christian bookshop.

In case of difficulty, please contact the publisher direct by writing to:

The Sales Department
KEVIN MAYHEW LTD
Buxhall
Stowmarket
Suffolk IP14 3BW

Phone 01449 737978
Fax 01449 737834
E-mail info@kevinmayhewltd.com

Please ask for our complete catalogue of outstanding Church Music.

First published in Great Britain in 1988 by Fountain Publications.
Reassigned to Kevin Mayhew Ltd. in 2002.

ISBN 1 84003 943 4
ISMN M 57024 101 9
Catalogue No: 1450256

1 2 3 4 5 6 7 8 9

Cover design by Jonathan Stroulger
Music editor and setter: Donald Thomson
Proof reader: Linda Ottewell

Printed and bound in Great Britain

On Christmas Eve, a group of young children find a fallen star lying in the street. Realising that it must be the Christmas Star (and, without its reappearance in the sky, there won't be any Christmas!) the children travel via the Policeman, the Astronomer and Santa Claus back to the very first Christmas Night.

Simple dialogue, verse speaking, original songs and favourite carols combine to make *Star of Wonder* the ideal Christmas production for younger children.

Cast

Andrew

Dawn

Farah

Louise

Owen

Roy

Policeman

Astronomer

Louise's Mum

Santa Claus

Angel

Mary

Joseph

Shepherds

Three Kings

Verse speaking group

Choir

Attendants, Angels,
Shepherd Boys –
as required.

Notes

The six children are named after youngsters who first performed the play in its present form. Teachers may prefer to let children use their own names.

The addition of a choir seated near the acting area not only enhances the singing on stage but also allows more children to participate. Songs for the Policeman, the Astronomer, Mum and Santa Claus need not be solos. In fact, if strong individual voices are not available, it may be safer to perform them as group items.

Please photocopy this page

KEVIN MAYHEW PERFORMANCE LICENCE FORM

We are delighted that you are considering *Star of Wonder* for production.
Please note that a performance licence is required and royalties are payable as follows:

10% of gross takings, plus VAT
(Minimum fee: £15.00 + VAT = £17.63)

This form should be returned to the Copyright Department at Kevin Mayhew Ltd. A copy, including our performance licence number, will be returned to you.

Name of Organisation ______________________________

Contact name ______________________________

Contact address ______________________________

____

Postcode ______________________________

Contact Telephone No. ______________ **Contact Fax No.** ______________

E-mail ______________________________

Date(s) of performance(s) ______________________________

Venue ______________________________

Seating capacity ______________________________

Proposed ticket price ______________________________

I undertake to submit performance fees due to Kevin Mayhew Ltd within 28 days of the last performance of *Star of Wonder*, together with a statement of gross takings.

Signature ______________________________

Name (please print) ______________________________

On behalf of ______________________________

Address if different from above ______________________________

____

- -

To be completed by Kevin Mayhew Copyright Department:

Performance Licence No. ______________ is issued to ______________________

for ________ performances of *Star of Wonder* on ______________________

Copyright Department, Kevin Mayhew Ltd, Buxhall, Stowmarket, Suffolk, IP14 3BW
Telephone number: UK 01449 737978 International +44 1449 737978
Fax number: UK 01449 737834 International +44 1449 737834
E-mail: info@kevinmayhewltd.com

Songs and Incidental Music

* Words and music: William James Kirkpatrick (1838-1921)
** Words and music: John Henry Hopkins (1820-1891)

for Colleen

STAR OF WONDER

Barry Hart

1. INTRODUCTION

21
C/G G C/G D/G G C/G D/G G
27
C/G G C/G G C/G G
32
C/G G C/G G
37
C/G G C/G D/G G C/G D/G
42
G C/G G C/G D/G G
47
C/G G N.C.
p
Guitar plays melody
f

The six CHILDREN enter and stand idly in groups; one or two throw a ball without much enthusiasm.

Verse Speakers It's Christmas Eve – the time is six
and bitter cold outside.
Look – here are children in the street
feeling bored, they kick their feet
and long for Christmastime.
It's Christmas Eve and getting late,
they don't know what to play.
If only morning time was here,
they've been waiting since last year
for this new Christmas Day.

Roy I know, let's play football.

Andrew Girls, do you want to play football?

Girls No, it's boring!

Dawn Let's play 'Cat's got the measles'!

Farah Then we can all join in.

Boys No thanks!

Owen Well, I'm fed up.

Louise So am I.

Roy Fed up waiting for Christmas Day!

Farah I'm waiting for a Barbie.

Andrew I'm waiting for a computer game.

Louise I'm waiting for rollerblades.

Dawn I'm waiting for new trainers.

Owen *(patting his tummy)* I'm waiting for my Christmas dinner!

All Roll on Christmas Day!

2. ROLL ON CHRISTMAS DAY

Lively (♩ = 126)
N.C.
mf
B♭ F/B♭ B♭ E♭/B♭ B♭
Capo 3 G D/G G C/G G
All mf
1. We're im - pa - tient, just can't wait, Mum says we can
2. Toys be - neath the Christ - mas tree, fav - 'rite pro - grammes
3. Pud - dings, tur - key and mince pies, oh, we won't be -
F/B♭ B♭ F/B♭ B♭ E♭ F
D/G G D/G G C D
stay up late. There will be good games to play – roll on Christ-mas
on T. V. All our cou - sins come to stay – roll on Christ-mas
lieve our eyes. We'll have fun in ev - 'ry way – roll on Christ-mas
Gm E♭ F B♭ B♭
Em C D G G
1, 3.
2.
3rd time to Coda
Day, roll on Christ - mas Day.
Day, roll on Christ - mas Day.
Day, roll on Christ - mas Day.

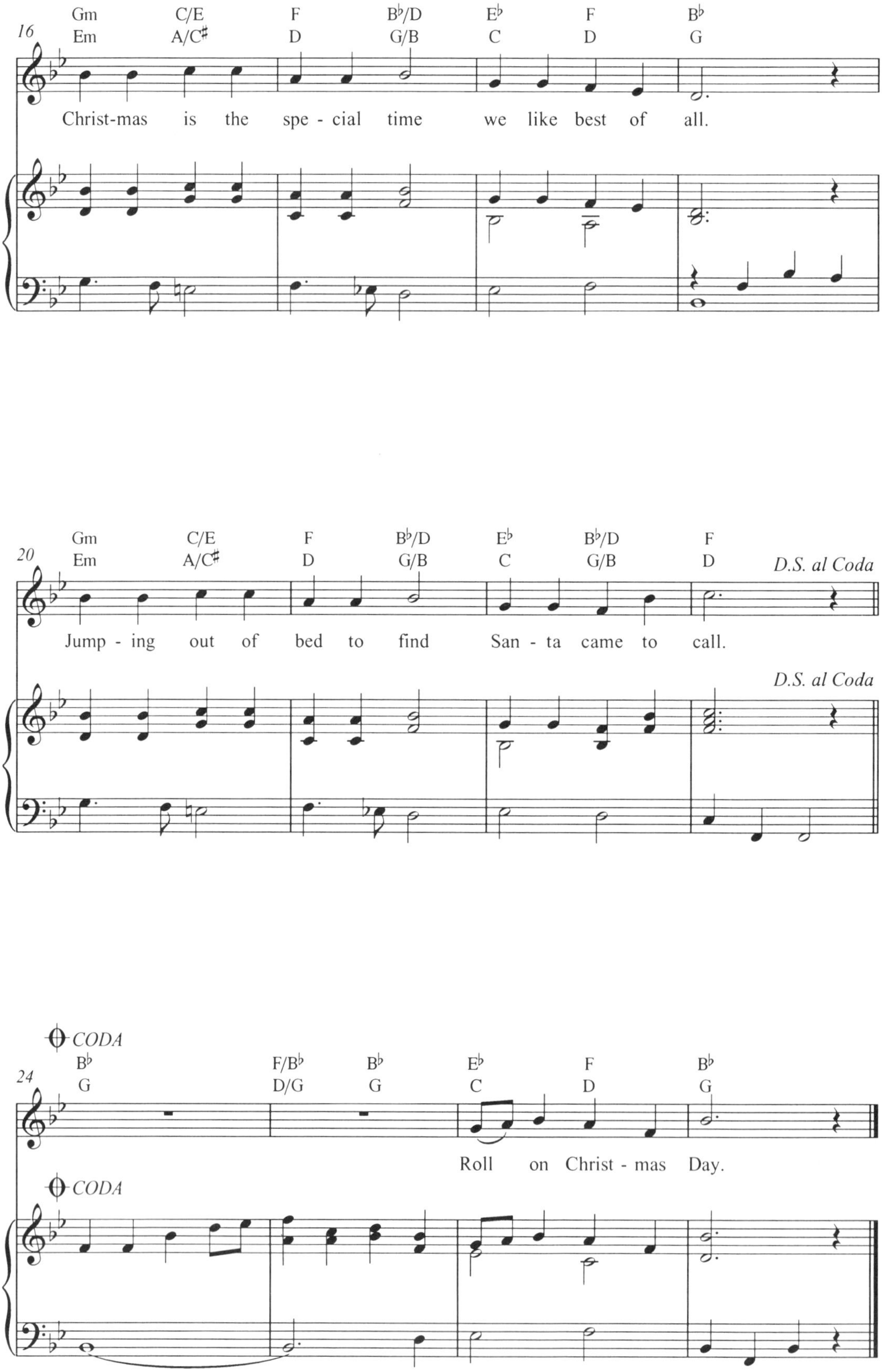
16
Gm C/E F B♭/D E♭ F B♭
Em A/C♯ D G/B C D G
Christ-mas is the spe - cial time we like best of all.
20
Gm C/E F B♭/D E♭ B♭/D F
Em A/C♯ D G/B C G/B D
D.S. al Coda
Jump - ing out of bed to find San - ta came to call.
D.S. al Coda
CODA
24
B♭ F/B♭ B♭ E♭ F B♭
G D/G G C D G
Roll on Christ - mas Day.
CODA

Owen Hey, look! There's something shining over there.

The CHILDREN run over, pick up the star and examine it.

Verse Speakers Just then – to their surprise,
in the road before their eyes
the children see –
can it really be?
They make a remarkable discovery.

Farah It's a star!

Roy *(looking up)* How did it get down here?

Owen It must have fallen from the sky.

Louise It's so beautiful!

Dawn But bigger than all the others.

Andrew This looks like a special star.

Roy Hold on – *(thinking)* – maybe this is the Christmas star.

Andrew The one the Kings followed to find Jesus?

Roy Yes.

Farah But how can we have Christmas without the Christmas Star?

Louise It needs to go back in the sky.

Dawn Or there won't be any Christmas.

All No more Christmas!

3. NO MORE CHRISTMAS

Chorus
E♭ C
E♭/D♭ C/B♭
A♭/C F/A
D7 B7
E♭/B♭ C/G
Got to get the star up high, high, high. Got to get the star up
1, 2.
3.
B♭ G
E♭ C
E♭/D♭ C/B♭
in the sky. in the sky. Got to get the star up
A♭/C F/A
D7 B7
E♭ C
B♭ G
E♭ C
high, high, high. Got to get the star up in the sky.

During the following verse, the CHILDREN, carrying the star, move towards the POLICEMAN who has entered, carrying a big, black book.

Verse Speakers No Christmas!
Just think –
no Christmas food and drink;
no presents!
Mum won't have a moment's peace.
It's just as well,
the children run to tell
the police.

Policeman Goodness gracious me! What's all this, then?

All Please, Sir, we've found a star.

Policeman You've found a what?

Andrew We've found a star.

Roy It's the Christmas Star.

Louise It needs to go back in the sky.

Dawn Or there won't be any Christmas.

Policeman Dear me, this is bad. I'll have a look in my book. *(opens the book and runs his finger down the page)* Was this star – parked on a yellow line?

All No.

Policeman Was this star – blocking the pavement?

All No.

Policeman Was this star – speeding along the High Street?

All No.

Policeman Then I'm sorry, children. *(slams book shut)* I can't help you.

4. THE POLICEMAN'S SONG

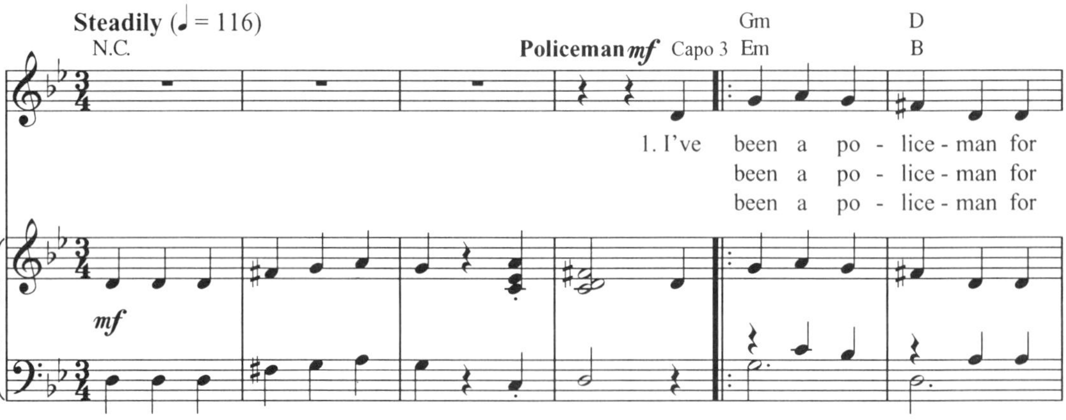

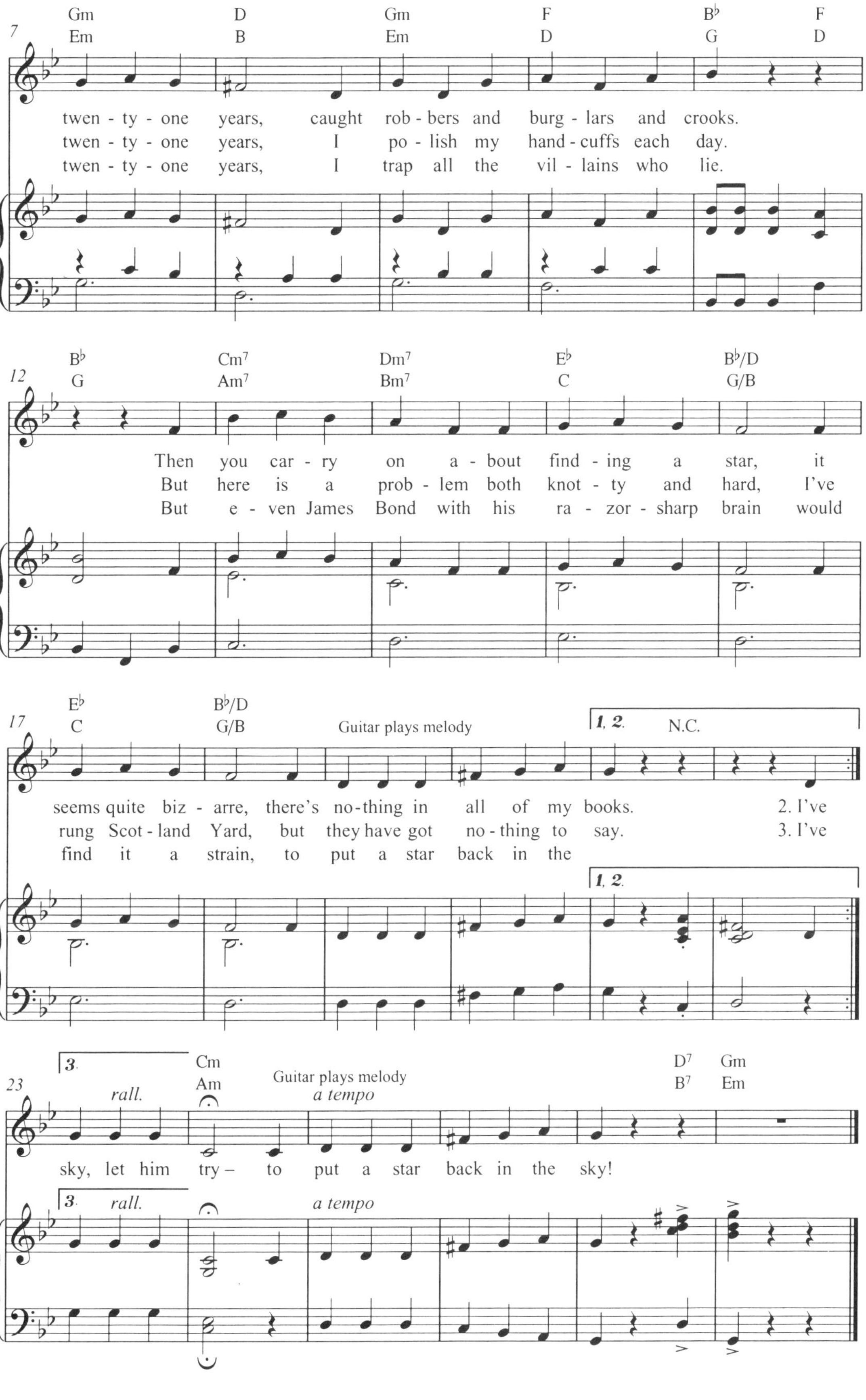
Gm D Gm F B♭ F
Em B Em D G D
twen - ty - one years, caught rob - bers and burg - lars and crooks.
twen - ty - one years, I po - lish my hand - cuffs each day.
twen - ty - one years, I trap all the vil - lains who lie.
B♭ Cm7 Dm7 E♭ B♭/D
G Am7 Bm7 C G/B
Then you car - ry on a - bout find - ing a star, it
But here is a prob - lem both knot - ty and hard, I've
But e - ven James Bond with his ra - zor - sharp brain would
E♭ B♭/D
C G/B
Guitar plays melody
1, 2.
N.C.
seems quite biz - arre, there's no - thing in all of my books. 2. I've
rung Scot - land Yard, but they have got no - thing to say. 3. I've
find it a strain, to put a star back in the
3.
rall.
Cm
Am
Guitar plays melody
a tempo
D7 Gm
B7 Em
sky, let him try – to put a star back in the sky!

Policeman Goodbye, children. *(he exits)*

Farah Oh dear! Now what are we going to do?

Andrew We need someone who knows about stars.

Dawn I know, why don't we go and see the astronomer?

Verse Speakers The children run to Station Street,
there's the house – number four,
now hammer loudly on the door.
Please, astronomer,
please be quick.
It's up to you to do the trick and try
to put the Star back in the sky.

Enter the ASTRONOMER, very irritable and slightly 'batty'. He carries a telescope.

Astronomer Jumping Jupiter! What's that you're carrying?

All Please, Sir, it's a star.

Owen It's fallen down.

Astronomer Nonsense, boy! Stars don't fall down.
(through his telescope, he searches the sky, vacantly)
Twinkle, twinkle little star,
I will watch you from afar.
If you fall I cannot cope,
there's nothing up my telescope!

Roy But it's the Christmas Star.

Louise It needs to go back in the sky.

Dawn Or there won't be any Christmas.

Astronomer Falling stars! I don't believe a word of it. Stuff and nonsense!

5. STARS SHOULD SHINE!

Moderately fast - crossly (♩ = 116)
N.C.
D
Capo 2 C
Astronomer mf
1. Stars should shine all the time, not fall to the ground.
2. Stars should shine all the time, what would peo - ple do
3. Stars should shine all the time, makes me scratch my head.
mf
C♯m7
Bm7
Stay up high, in the sky where they can be found.
if the sun, just for fun, star - ted tum - bling too?
When they're found, rol - ling round, in the street in - stead.
F♯m
Em
Bm7
Am7
E7
D7
A
G
Last time to Coda
Makes you cross, they'll get lost if they fall down.
No sun - tans, de - sert sands, what a to - do.
What a nerve, quite ab - surd, makes me see red!
Last time to Coda

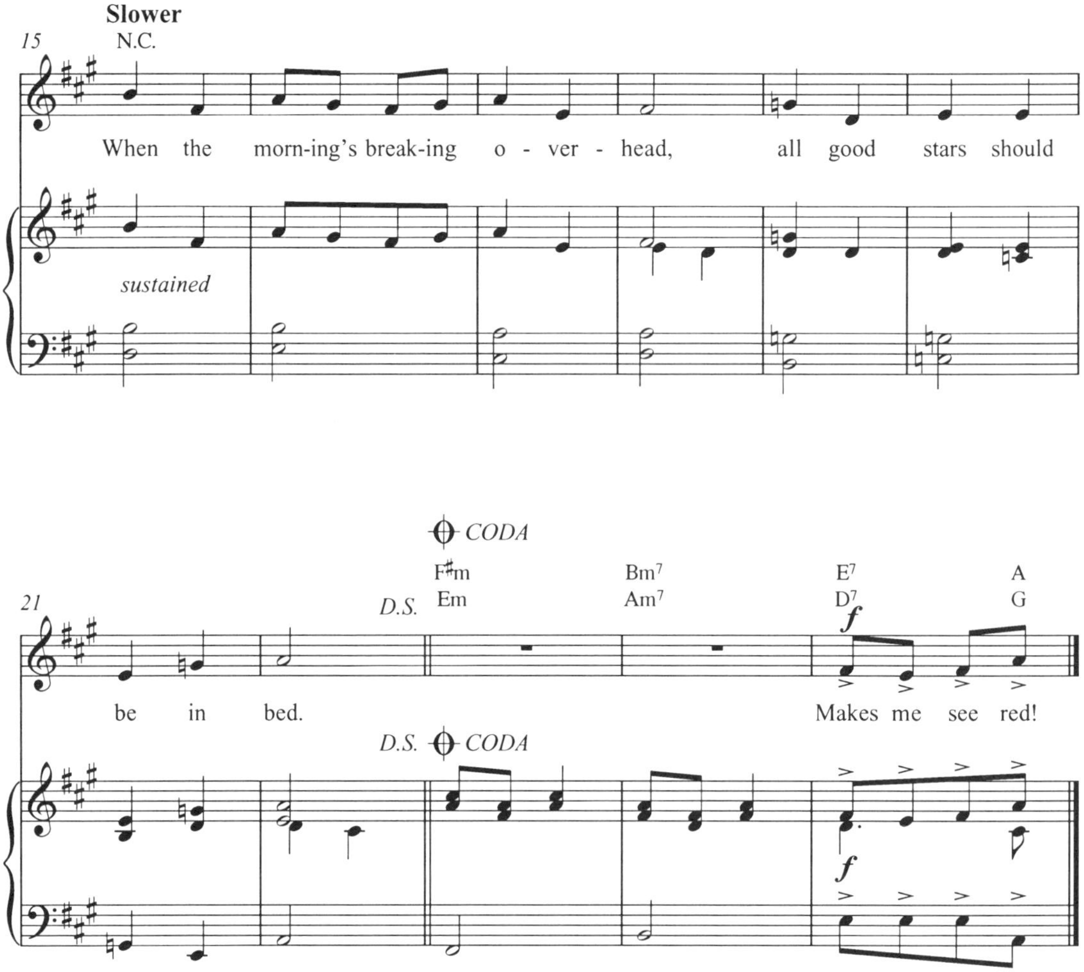
Slower
15
N.C.
When the morn-ing's break-ing o - ver - head, all good stars should
sustained
21
D.S.
CODA
F♯m Em
Bm7 Am7
E7 D7
A G
f
be in bed.
Makes me see red!
D.S. CODA
f

The ASTRONOMER exits, tut-tutting to himself.

Andrew He was hopeless!

Farah And time's running out.

Louise Come on, let's go and ask my Mum – she'll know what to do.

Verse Speakers Only an hour or two more
to try and save Christmas.
The children are sure
that Louise's Mum will know exactly what
should be done.

Enter MUM wearing her apron and carrying a mixing bowl and wooden spoon.

Louise Mum! Mum! Look what we've found!

Mum Very nice, dear, but I'm busy.

Owen It's the Christmas Star.

Mum Christmas! You don't have to tell me it's Christmas.

Louise But, Mum . . .

Mum Cakes to bake, turkey to stuff, decorations to put up.

Roy But it's the Christmas Star.

Louise It needs to go back in the sky.

Dawn Or there won't be any Christmas.

Mum If I don't get these pies baked, there *definitely* won't be any Christmas.

6. MUM'S MERRY CHRISTMAS

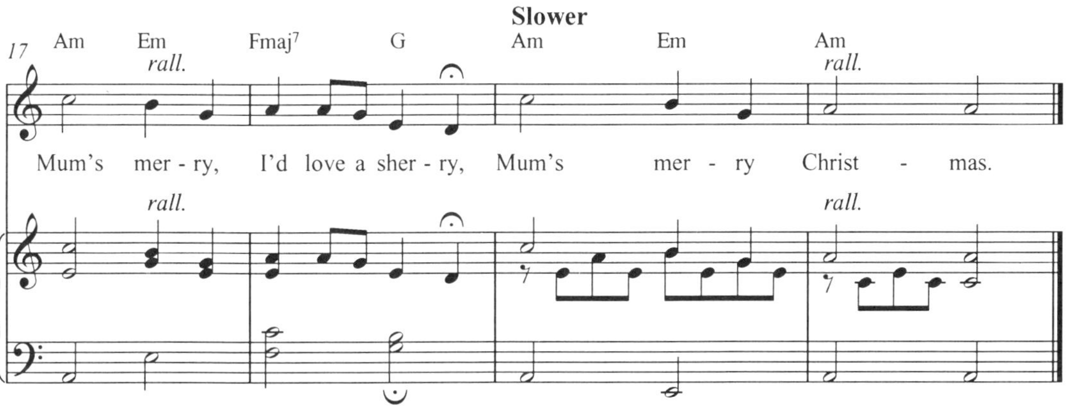

MUM starts to exit, but turns back to say:

Mum And don't leave that star in the hall – ask your Dad to fix it to the Christmas tree.

MUM exits

Verse Speakers Poor Mum – lots to do,
but now they'll never succeed.
Who knows about Christmas Stars?
An expert is what they need.

Roy I wish Santa was here to help us.

Dawn We don't know where to find him.

Owen Yes, we do, I saw him last week at the grotto in Dobson's Store.

Andrew Maybe he's still packing up his sleigh.

Farah Come on! We've got to hurry.

They rush across to SANTA who enters and sits down gloomily, rubbing his feet.

All Hello, Santa.

Santa Oh hello, children.

Owen You look miserable. What's up?

Santa I'm getting too old for this job and my poor feet ache!

Farah But Santa, this is an emergency!

Roy We've found the Christmas Star.

Louise It needs to go back in the sky.

Dawn Or there won't be any Christmas.

Santa Do you know, that might not be such a bad idea.

7. SANTA WON'T BE ROUND TOMORROW NIGHT

Swing tempo (♩ = 110)
B♭ Bdim F/C D7 G/B C
mf
4 F C7 Santa mf F A7
1. I've got a lot of prob - lems but no - bo - dy knows,
got a lot of prob - lems, why's it al - ways me?
got a lot of prob - lems, here's a dir - ty trick:
7 Dm F7 B♭ Bdim
can't get bat - ter - ies for Ru - dolph's nose. I don't want to scare you or
Now the sleigh has failed its M. O. T. Got a spot of rust and a
doc - tor says the gnomes have gone down sick. Who will pack the toys up? It
Last time to Coda
10 F/C D7 G/B C 1. F C7
give you a fright – San - ta won't be round to - mor - row night. 2. I've
dod - gy back light – San - ta won't be round to - mor - row
just is - n't right –
Last time to Coda
1.

2.
13 F F7 B♭ F/A C F A7/E
night. I'm not get - ting young - er, that's for sure;
16 Dm A7 Dm B♭ F/A C F D7/F♯
I should be slow-ing down by rights. It's al - ways freez - ing out of doors and I'm
20 G G/F C D.S. al Coda CODA G/B C
tired of work- ing nights. 3. I've San - ta won't be round to - mor - row
23 F D7 G/B C F
night. San - ta won't be round to - mor - row night.
8vb

Dawn This is terrible!

Roy Santa, you must deliver all the presents.

Louise Think of all the sad children.

Owen It's bad enough having no star.

Andrew But no Santa as well!

SANTA rises slowly to his feet.

Santa Do you know, I think I might just make it.

8. SANTA WILL BE ROUND TOMORROW NIGHT

Swing tempo (♩ = 110)
B♭ Bdim F/C D7 G/B C
mf
4 F C7 Santa mf F A7
I'd bet - ter make an ef - fort, got to tra - vel far,
7 Dm F7 B♭ Bdim
there's no time to help you with your star. All the lit - tle child - ren had

10 F/C D7 G/B C F D7
bet - ter sleep tight – San - ta will be round to - mor - row night (I did - n't mean it),
13 G/B C F D7
San - ta will be round to - mor - row night (so hang your socks up),
15 G/B C F F/E♭
San - ta will be round to - mor - row night.
18 B♭/D B♭m/D♭ F/C N.C.
8vb

Santa Thank you, children, I'm feeling quite perky again. Goodbye!

SANTA throws his sack over his shoulder and exits.

Farah Well, that's it.

Owen I give up.

All No more Christmas.

As the introductory music plays, the ANGEL enters and speaks over the music.

Angel Dear children – you have tried so hard. Come, follow me and I will help you to discover the real meaning of Christmas. Together we will return the star to the sky and its light will shine down on a tiny child whose love lit the world on the first Christmas night.

During the song the children, led by the ANGEL, 'travel' back to the stable and join the Nativity scene to kneel by the manger. NB: the KINGS have yet to arrive.

9. THE FIRST CHRISTMAS NIGHT / AWAY IN A MANGER

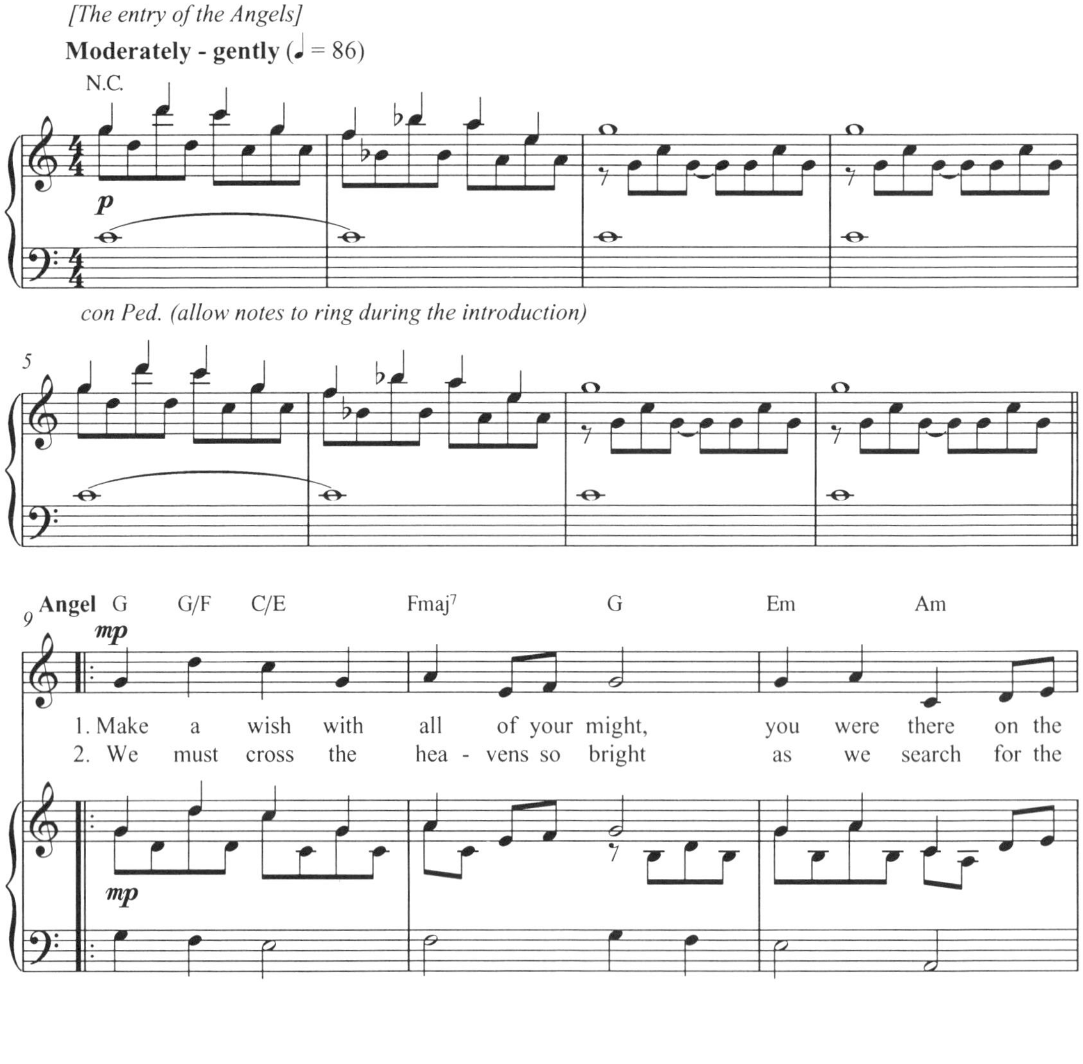
[The entry of the Angels]
Moderately - gently (♩ = 86)
N.C.
p
con Ped. (allow notes to ring during the introduction)
5
9 Angel G G/F C/E Fmaj7 G Em Am
mp
1. Make a wish with all of your might, you were there on the
2. We must cross the hea - vens so bright as we search for the
mp

12 Dm G G/F C/E Cdim Em
first Christ-mas night. Take my hand, we leave right a - way,
first Christ-mas night. Sil - ver star - light will be our guide,
15 D/C G/B 1. Am7 D G 2. Am7 D G All
off to find Je - sus sleep-ing in the hay.
right to the place where ba - by Je - sus lies. We'll
18 Gm/E A7 Dm A7 Dm Am B7
gradual cresc. for 4 bars
go through the win - ter wind so cold, we'll go though we are not
21 Em D7 G C/E G/D Dm7 G/D
f ben marcato
ve - ry old un - til we look up in the sky; see the

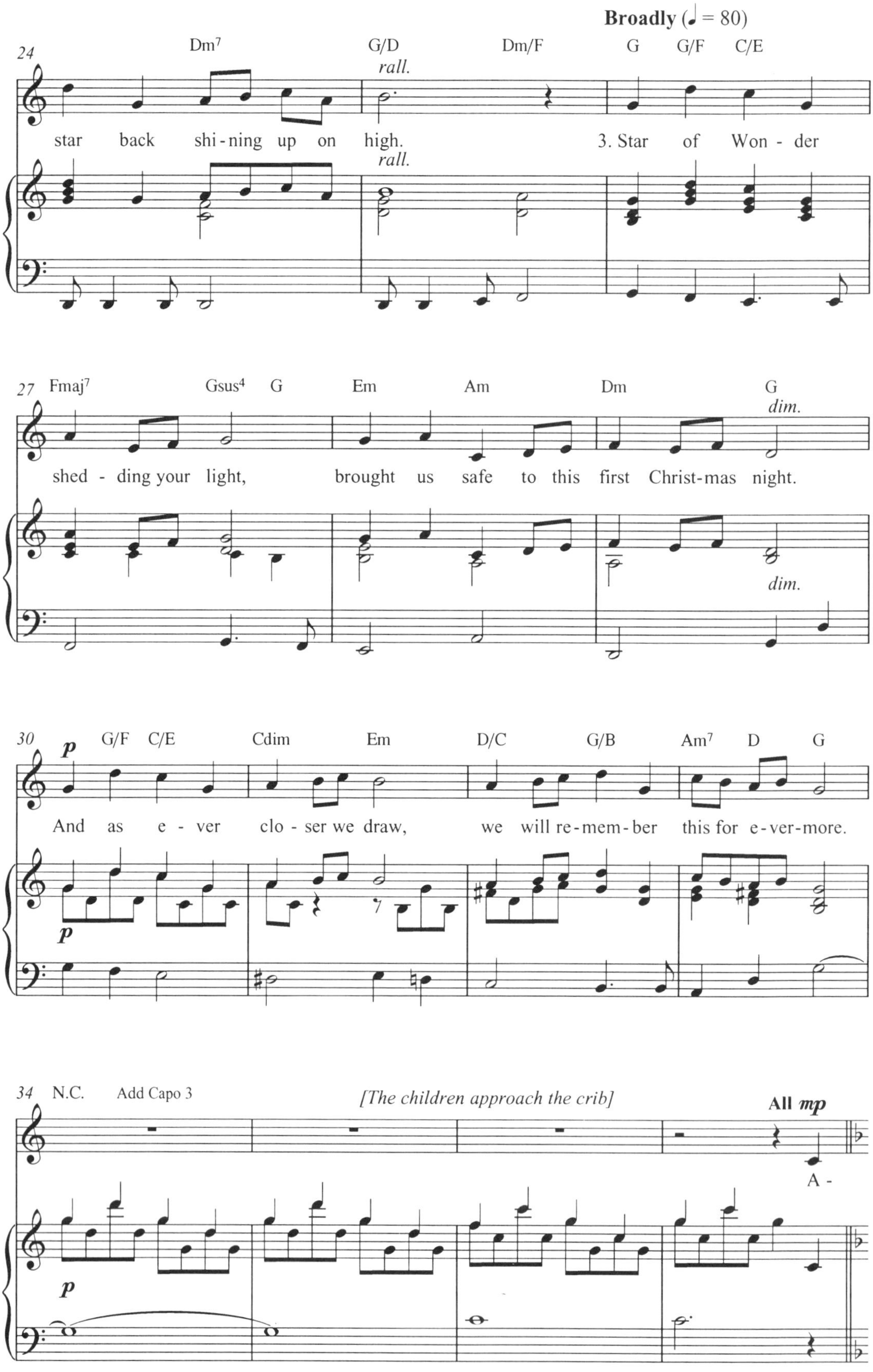
Broadly (♩ = 80)
24
Dm7 G/D Dm/F G G/F C/E
rall.
star back shi-ning up on high. 3. Star of Won-der
rall.
27
Fmaj7 Gsus4 G Em Am Dm G
dim.
shed-ding your light, brought us safe to this first Christ-mas night.
dim.
30
G/F C/E Cdim Em D/C G/B Am7 D G
p
And as e-ver clo-ser we draw, we will re-mem-ber this for e-ver-more.
p
34
N.C. Add Capo 3
[The children approach the crib]
All mp
A-
p

With a gentle lilt
The CHILDREN and the ANGEL return the star
and everyone watches as it rises slowly in the sky.
38
Capo 3
F D
Gm Em
way in a man - ger, no crib for a bed, the
mp
42
C A
F D
G E
G7 E7
C A
lit - tle Lord Je - sus laid down his sweet head. The
46
F D
F7 D7
B♭ G
stars in the bright sky looked down where he lay, the
50
Gm Em
Dm Bm
F/A D/F♯
B♭6 G6
poco rall.
C7 A7
F D
lit - tle Lord Je - sus a - sleep in the hay.
poco rall.

10. WE THREE KINGS

The KINGS and their attendants now enter in grand procession and make their way to the stable as all the children and the audience sing.

Moderate processional tempo - very grand (♪ = 128)
N.C.
f
9
All f
Em B7 Em B7 Em
We three kings of O-ri-ent are; bear-ing gifts we tra-verse a-far.
17
D G Am E/B B7 Em
Field and foun-tain, moor and moun-tain, fol-low-ing yon-der star.
24
D7 G D/F♯ Em C G
O star of won-der, star of night, star with

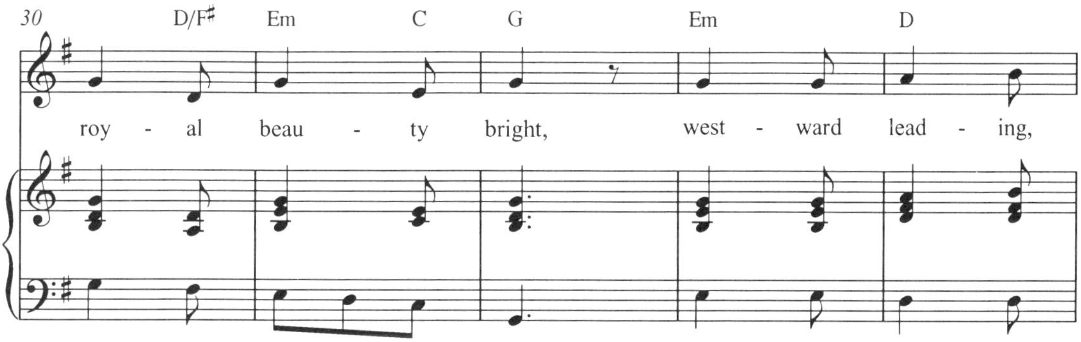
30
D/F♯ Em C G Em D
roy - al beau - ty bright, west - ward lead - ing,

35
C G Dsus4 D6 Em C G/B C G
still pro - ceed - ing, guide us to thy per - fect light.

Verse Speakers Christmas is saved – the star is on high,
back where it should be up in the sky.
If you look very hard on Christmas night
you may see it shedding its light
on a cold winter world where God sends his Son,
and the star will smile down –
Christmas has come.

11. STAR OF WONDER

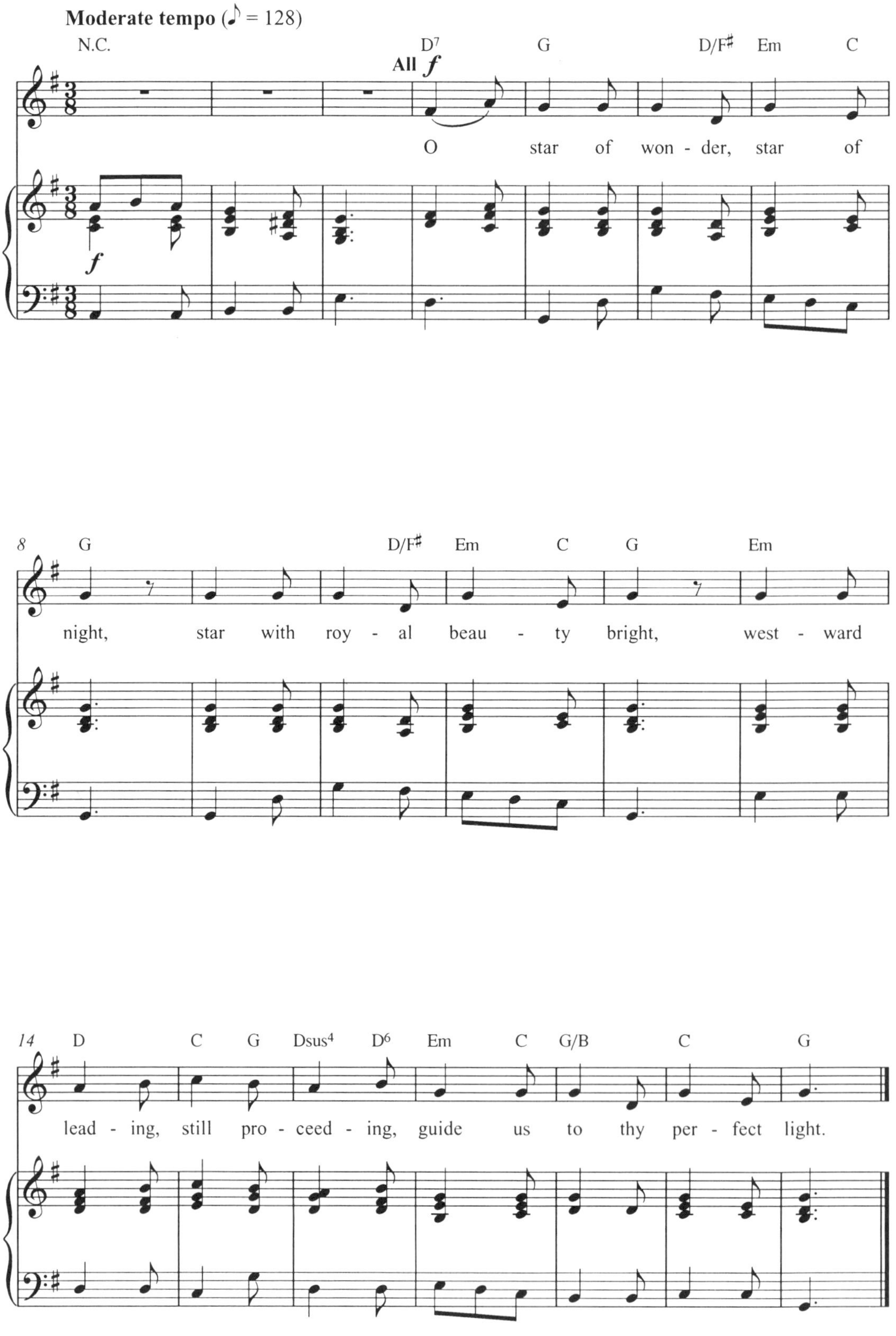
Moderate tempo (♪ = 128)
N.C. D7 G D/F♯ Em C
All f
O star of won - der, star of
f
8 G D/F♯ Em C G Em
night, star with roy - al beau - ty bright, west - ward
14 D C G Dsus4 D6 Em C G/B C G
lead - ing, still pro - ceed - ing, guide us to thy per - fect light.